STARTERS FOR CLARINET

GORDON LEWIN

THE ASSOCIATED BOARD OF
THE ROYAL SCHOOLS OF MUSIC

MELODY

from *Lucrezia Borgia*, Prologue

DONIZETTI

LADY OWEN'S DELIGHT

WELSH FOLKSONG

AB 2233

CELEBRATION DANCE

GORDON LEWIN

'I HAD A LITTLE DOVE'

CZECH FOLKTUNE

AB 2233

TWO SPANISH FOLKSONGS

En lo alto de aquella montaña

(In that mountain height)

from LEON

El Cortejo

(Courting)

from ASTURIAS

AMORETTEN TANZE

(Dance of the little Cupids)

JOSEPH GUNGL

SLY PATRICK

IRISH FOLKSONG

MARCH

from *Alceste*

GLUCK

22/5/00

CASTILIAN SONG

SWEET SORROW

GORDON LEWIN

LA BIONDINA

(The fair-haired girl)

TRADITIONAL VENETIAN SONG

DANCE

from *Preciosa*

WEBER

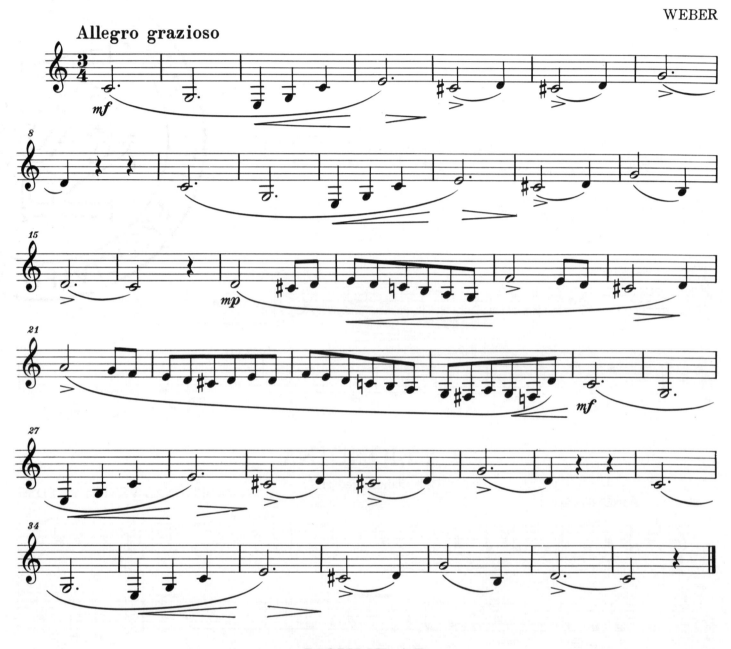

USKUDAR

TURKISH FOLKTUNE

BERCEUSE

ILYNSKY

HEIDENRÖSLEIN
(Moorland rose)

SCHUBERT

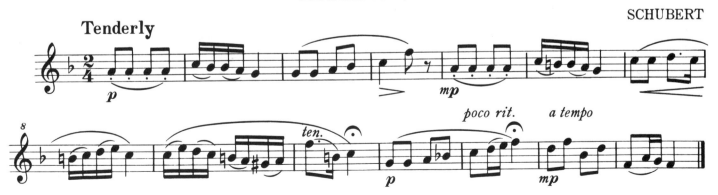

PAWS FOR THOUGHT

GORDON LEWIN

Moderato–Jazzy and jaunty, but stealthily

THE GROVES OF BLARNEY

IRISH FOLKSONG

Andante moderato

SIESTA

Based on traditional Central American Dances
from El Salvador and Guatemala

Andante ma ritmico

THE LARK IN THE CLEAR AIR

IRISH FOLKSONG

Andante

sempre molto cantabile

'WIENER BLUT' WALTZ No. 1

JOHANN STRAUSS

Moderato

'À QUEL ÂGE EST-ON GRANDE?'

('When do you become grown up?')

L. CLAPISSON

Allegretto

PUFFING BILLY

GORDON LEWIN

Slow, a steady blues tempo

EN PASSANT PAR LA LORRAINE

(Passing through Lorraine)

FRENCH TRADITIONAL SONG

Tempo marziale

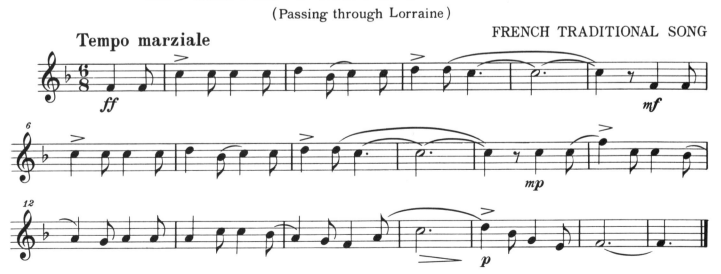

THE PLAINTIVE NIGUN*

ISRAELI FOLKSONG

Andantino

* A song of deep or spiritual significance

MARIA CATLINA

PIEDMONTESE FOLKSONG
(18th century)

Andante

EL TRÍPILI*

SPANISH TONADILLA
(18th century)

Allegretto

* This is a nonsense word in Spanish.

HOT CROSS BUNS

OLD LONDON STREET CRY

Moderato

PORTRAIT CHARMANT

TRADITIONAL FRENCH TUNE

Allegretto

A HUNDRED PIPERS

TRADITIONAL SCOTTISH TUNE

Alla marcia

PIERROT SHOW

GORDON LEWIN

Allegro

'O MON CHER AMANT'

('O my dear loved one')
from *La Périchole*

OFFENBACH

Andante

BUNCH OF ROSES

IRISH FOLKSONG
(c.1812)

Slow and dignified

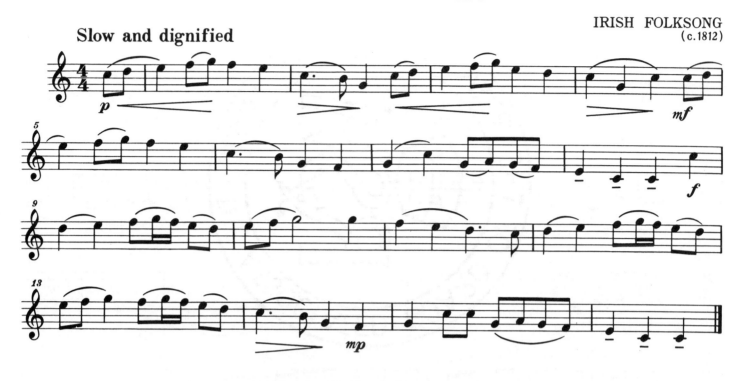

TOBAGO SUNSET

GORDON LEWIN

Andante con moto

AIR

from *Der Freischütz*, Act III finale

WEBER

TIVIOT BRIDGE

OLD SCOTTISH REEL

CARAMBA

Based on two Mexican folksongs

'JOHNNY HAS GONE FOR A SOLDIER'

SONG OF THE AMERICAN REVOLUTION

MICAELA'S ARIA
from *Carmen*, Act III

BIZET

BUBBLE AND SQUEAK

GORDON LEWIN

'ROW WEEL, MY BOATIE, ROW WEEL'

ROBERT SMITH

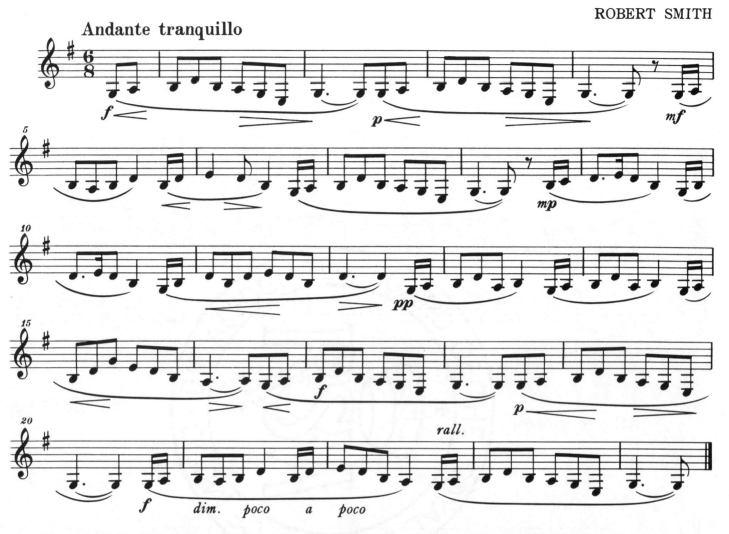

'WAVES OF THE DANUBE', WALTZ No.1

IVANOVICI

HOPE THE HERMIT

TRADITIONAL ENGLISH TUNE
(17th century)

ANDANTE
from 'Kreutzer' Sonata, Op.47

BEETHOVEN

AFTER HOURS

GORDON LEWIN

Moderato—Beguine tempo

AB 2233

Reproduced and printed by
Halstan & Co. Ltd., Amersham, Bucks., England